YOUNG AUTHORS OF AMERICA

VOLUME FOUR

1991

Edited and
With an Introduction by
ELLEN RUDIN

Published by The Trumpet Club
666 Fifth Avenue, New York, New York 10103

ISBN 0-440-84367-7

Printed in the United States of America
Designed by Kohar Alexanian
January 1992

10 9 8 7 6 5 4 3 2 1
OPM

CONTENTS

Introduction

POETRY WINNERS

(in random order)

INTRODUCTION

The Young Authors of America Contest has become, like certain flowers, a hardy perennial, coming up year after year. Seeds sown long ago continue to bring forth new generations of splendid blooms. This year more than six thousand young people sent in their stories, essays, and poems—a garden of delights.

As in previous years, the children wrote about the things that matter most to them: their homes and families, schools, friends, pets, and possessions; their wants, longings, and dreams; their joys, successes, disappointments, and sorrows. Some tried their hand at genre forms—mysteries, fairy tales, fantasies, and science fiction—and some wrote just for fun. Perhaps because of the country's recent involvement in the Persian Gulf war, many entries dealt with war and with the possibility—or reality—of death, and with the fear of separation, and with loss. A lot of nonfiction pieces turned up this year, including reminiscences both happy and sad. Yet, as always, these writings overall confirmed the tremendous resiliency of children, their essential good will and good humor, and their large capacity for hope.

From the abundant harvest came first, second,

and third place winners and eight runners-up. For the second year in a row, so many fine poems emerged that a special poetry section is included in the book. All the winning entries are published here in full. In addition, the names of seventy-seven young writers, whose work received honorable mention, are listed on the final pages.

The winning manuscripts represent an exciting array of young talent. In "Almost an Angel," a true story, Erin Ashley Williamson remembers with poignancy and sharp feeling the death of a gentle classmate whose brief illness disturbs and saddens his friends. Michael H. Shecket's reflective "Places We'd Like To Be" tells about the start of a friendship between two boys who, thrown together in a new school, each miss their former cities and homes. Kathy Goebel's comical tale, "The Musical Frog," about a pet that inspires its young owner to the concert stage, is both wistful and funny. "Letters to Home: Viet Nam" by Carl Grayson Bell, Jr., details the shocking toll that war takes on one American family; and Nicole Peterson's witty "World War Three: The End" takes the reader not very far into the future to a surprising place.

In Justin Scott Ball's engrossing "The Van Fire," a true account, the author talks with affection about his lifelong experiences with the family van, now destroyed by an engine fire. "Why I Whine When I Do" by Bridget Michelle Faugot describes humorously the fine art of getting one's way. A better world than we have now is imagined in

Taylor Allison Nolen's affecting essay, "The Easy World." Clair Null's "Bird Buffet" explores the warm relationship between an elderly resident of a nursing home and the young volunteer who loves to visit her.

A girl who thinks, incredulously, that she has seen the tombstone of Santa Claus in the cemetery where her grandfather is buried goes back to take a wary second look in "What? Santa's Grave?" by Kristina Cavallo. Jonathan Simmons remembers his birth mother in his moving true story, "She Said She Was Coming Back."

The poetry section, a little garden of its own, is filled with perceptive poems that celebrate nature and the outdoors and that probe the human spirit through friendship, courage, self-determination, and understanding.

One young writer said of her submission to the contest, "This story was based on what most children think of at some time or other in their life." I thought, How true. In fact, how true it is that all of the contest entries, winners and otherwise, were about the things that children think of. Writing is, after all, a means to communicate, to share our thoughts and feelings. The thousands of girls and boys who entered this year's contest shared themselves, as true writers do. Thanks and congratulations to every one of you.

Ellen Rudin
July 1991

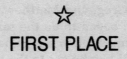

FIRST PLACE

ALMOST AN ANGEL

A True Story, 1989–1990

by Erin Ashley Williamson

To Justin Kyle Jernigan
—may he rise

Chapter One

HERE COMES CAT!

"Here comes Cat!" T.J. mimicked as Justin came down the road.

It was all my fault. Justin, being so far away, had looked like a cat to me. So I leaned over to Rachel and said, "Here comes a cat."

Rachel sighed. "That's not a cat—that's Justin."

T.J. had overheard. He started doing cartwheels and backflips, roaring with laughter. While he did this, he rang out, "Justin the cat! Justin the cat!"

Jeff, Amanda, Greg, and Matthew, who thought T.J. was a king, began to do the same thing.

Justin was a small, silent sort of boy, and usually very peaceful. When he got to the bus stop, there were tears in his eyes.

Soon our bus came. We all hopped on, Justin at the end of the line. As the bus puttered down the road to our school, Indian Creek, I looked out the east window at the orange and pink sunrise.

About five or six minutes later I saw our school cover up the sunrise. I headed toward the gym because we had all gotten to school too early.

Some people ran into the gym. Some walked. Some trudged. Some skipped. I strutted across the gym floor to the third-grade-girls' line. I lunged to the end. Although it wasn't a long line, I despised being at the end of any line. It's not especially that I wanted to be at the front of the line. The middle would be all right.

I looked at the middle of the boys' line. Justin was there, for the *first* time.

As more and more people came into the gymnasium, it got louder and louder. And Justin got quieter and quieter.

Soon the bell rang, sounding like an overly excited child. Our line was let out after the fourth-grade-boys' line.

As usual, I headed straight down the hall to Miss Ballard's class.

Chapter Two

THE UNPLEASANT SURPRISE

A few mornings later, when I went into Miss Ballard's room, she was . . . crying. Justin's mom was in the room. Justin was holding her hand tightly. He had a patch over his left eye. He looked scared. Very scared. And very confused.

I sat down at my desk after I had rapidly put my bookbag and lunch box in locker number 19.

I looked at the worried faces of Miss Ballard, Mrs. Jernigan, and Justin. Then I looked at everyone else in the room. They seemed frantic with fear and concern. Now I had an awful thought nagging in the back of my head. It struck me like this: What happened? Did Justin get hurt? Why is everyone scared? Why is Miss Ballard crying?

All at once, feeling quite upset, I shouted out, "WHAT HAPPENED?"

Everyone turned to stare at me. I felt embarrassed. I also felt a lump in my throat as Mrs. Jernigan and Justin slipped out of the room and I guess out of the school. I felt a buildup of tears in my eyes grow bigger and my voice trail away. Everyone waited for an honest answer. Miss Ballard hesitated and got up.

She began, "Justin . . ." She stopped. "Has cancer . . . in the back . . . of his . . ." She was pausing so much it was driving me *crazy*. "His head," she finally said. I gasped along with the others.

A cluster of tears skidded down my cheeks. I could feel my face turn bright pink in embarrassment. I looked around. Everyone looked back at me with very anxious eyes. All eyes were a little wet, some even wetter than mine. I could hear my heartbeat echo around the room. Suddenly I felt like the world had come to an end.

When I got home and told my mom, she said she knew already. Apparently, Miss Ballard had called the homes of everyone in our class.

Chapter Three

IN BED

As I lay in bed that night and listened in the cold, I could hear my mom telling my dad details I know she wouldn't ever have told me.

"Poor Justin. He must be scared."

"What happened?"

"Well, Miss Ballard noticed that his eyes weren't tracking right. She sent him to the nurse, but the nurse. . . ." I closed my eyes and put my hands over my ears.

My eyes shot open. I had wept myself to sleep. I listened. Nothing. Everyone at 1944 Westminster was asleep. I tried to go back to sleep. I just couldn't. I kept thinking about Justin and how sweet he was.

"He stopped many fights at our bus stop," I said to myself. I could picture Justin holding up his hands and saying, "Stop fighting!" I smiled a little. But then I wondered. Was Justin sleeping right now? Or was he awake and worrying, like me?

Later I felt someone come and sit beside me. It was my dad. He was laughing. "Wake up, lazybones," he said.

For some reason my breakfast didn't taste so delicious, and my toothbrush didn't seem to clean so well. I didn't care what clothes I put on.

Things were changing.

Chapter Four

LONELINESS

It had been over three weeks. Justin was not at school. He hadn't been. I glanced over at his empty desk. His locker seemed to be lonely for him.

"I've got wonderful news. Justin is coming to school today," said Miss Ballard.

Megan, a red-haired, freckle-faced, blue-eyed, lively girl, clapped her hands together in excitement.

Justin walked into the room. Everyone looked at him. Justin wore a hat because, we found out later, one part of his head was bald. His medicine had made him chubby and a bit yellowish.

He began, "I haven't been at school because I was in the hospital. I got to go into a funnel-shaped room, only it was on its side. They used a laser to kill the cancer. It made a big sound, but I didn't care because it sounded like a machine gun." (He loved the army and wanted to be a pilot.)

Just then he remembered something. "And I go two times a day, every day."

The hours went by too quickly.

"Now Justin has to go for his treatment," Miss Ballard said, regretfully.

"Bye, Justin," I said as he walked out of the room. Other people echoed me. "Bye, Justin. See ya soon!" they called.

Chapter Five

FREE

"He's gonna die and you want him to!" Leslie said to Lance. How dare she! Lance was in Scouts with Justin! (They were best friends, too!)

"No, he won't die!" I screamed at Leslie, my voice echoing through the classroom and into the hall.

Miss Ballard told us about Justin's cancer. It was

getting worse. Now he could barely hear. I felt very ill when I heard this. I was beginning to cry, but I was embarrassed. I tried not to make a peep, but I ended up choking. Miss Ballard rushed me over to the fountain. I gulped the water. I looked up. Miss Ballard was smiling down on me with her brown, sparkling eyes. I hugged her.

After school my bus dropped me off a little late at our bus stop. I trudged slowly home. Usually it only took me five or six minutes from the bus stop, but that day it took ten. Rachel and the rest of the gang had gotten way ahead of me.

I took the key off my neck. I placed the key in the keyhole.

To my surprise, the door opened by itself; my mom had gotten home before me. I put my key and lunch box on the counter. My mom gave me a nice, big hug. I sat down at the breakfast nook table to have a light snack and rest.

Meanwhile my dad came home. We had supper, and after a while we went to bed.

I slept soundly.

Chapter Six

THERE'S ALWAYS HOPE

It was September fifth. It was going to be *hot*. I put my jacket away.

At school we were doing math. On the bus ride home, I just looked out the window.

Off the bus, at 3:35, I began another endless journey toward home. Part of the way there, I decided to go see how Justin was doing.

I rang the doorbell. The sound seemed to come and go with the simmering wind. Slowly the door opened. A woman that looked exactly like Justin's mother stepped out, but she was shorter.

"Mrs. Jernigan?" I asked worriedly when I saw her face.

"I'm not Mrs. Jernigan. I'm Justin's aunt," she began. "You know, Justin is very sick," she said. She paused. Her eyes shone pink in the sun. I knew she was going to cry.

I looked in their window. The whole family was there. And waiting.

I turned toward Justin's aunt. She just smiled at me.

"Thank you for coming," she said. She opened up the huge front door. "Bye."

I watched her go inside.

I *ran* the rest of the way home.

At 3:40, I found my mom already at home. She gravely walked over to me. I think I knew what I was going to hear.

A voice echoed in my head: "There's always hope."

Chapter Seven

NOTHING CAN HARM HIM NOW

"Honey, Justin isn't going to be riding your bus anymore," my mother said. I knew what she meant.

"But Justin's aunt . . ." I said, gripping her arm.

"She didn't want to say how bad things really were," she told me.

I collapsed in her arms. "He didn't!" I cried. "Just didn't!"

That night I dreamt that an angel came down to me and said, "Justin is safe. Do not worry."

The angel then smiled at me and disappeared.

Flowers began to grow on the white background. I felt at home.

I opened my eyes and sat up. The room was dark. I wondered what Justin was doing.

Author's Note: *I first met Justin in third grade. In mid-March of that school year, people began to notice that Justin wasn't doing so well.*

On September 5, 1990, Justin died. I wrote this story to show how special he was to me and many others.

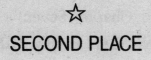

SECOND PLACE

PLACES WE'D LIKE TO BE

by Michael H. Shecket

*To Mrs. Londergan, all of my friends,
and especially Samuel Greenspan*

Chapter 1

". . . a good student . . ."

Miguel Herman Samuels, Jr., sat on the stage of the auditorium at the Beverly Hills Academy for Boys, envisioning his father dressed in his lab suit.

". . . set a fine example for our boys . . ."

He looked down upon the bald head of a man standing in the aisle, talking into a microphone. Miguel could almost sense the way the crowd of more than five hundred students and teachers saw him, champion of the world, hero of the day.

". . . won national geography and spelling bees . . ."

He sat silently on a chair bearing the insignia of the school, thinking about anything but the Student of the Year award he was about to receive.

". . . please give a round of applause for the winner of this year's award, Mike Samuels."

Miguel nearly tripped over a wire as he stood up to accept his award from the dean of students. He clumsily pulled out his notes for his speech from his jacket. He began to talk, babbling on about the school, the teachers. But his mind was really on other things.

Chapter 2

Miguel could still picture the first place he ever lived, the white house with the pretty blue shutters at 4026 Bushnell Road in University Heights, Ohio. He lived next to an old man who had many grandchildren who visited on occasion. On the other side lived his friend Ted, who scared him out of his wits when they used to go to the park and swing on the swings.

He also remembered playing with his friend Dave Greenspan on Tuesdays. He used to love to make up stories and act them out with Dave. They liked going to museums together on Saturdays.

One of his fondest memories was going to the Workman's Circle School on Sundays, where his grandfather taught Yiddish music. Miguel loved to sing, and once got angry when his Papa Samuels refused to give him a solo part in a concert. Later he was able to understand that he really couldn't sing well enough when he was just four years old.

He remembered Carl the barber, who died in a fishing accident, mailing letters at the box at the corner, and the place he went to kindergarten: De Soto Magnet Elementary School.

He remembered the fuss over moving to Columbus for his dad's new job at Grant Hospital. His dad worked there almost seven years before he died. Miguel used to like to walk to Worthington Square Mall after school with his friends Eric, Jeremy, Joe, and Kent. Joe really liked rap music and did this weird beat box routine where he'd stand in the corner of a room and make strange noises. That was hilarious to Miguel.

He remembered Worthingvillage Elementary School, or WES for short. The principal, Mr. Bench, had a joke about the initials. "WE'S the best!" he'd say.

Suddenly becoming conscious of his surroundings, Miguel listened to his own words as he droned on almost automatically.

". . . atmosphere of this excellent California school. Under those peculiar circumstances, I had the . . ."

I said that? he thought. He then returned to his recollective trance.

Chapter 3

He winced as he imagined his father fall over the steering wheel of the car, gripping his chest and making a pathetic screeching noise. He hadn't seen it himself, but he had played it out in his mind a million times. When his father had his heart attack, it changed Miguel's life forever.

He remembered checking his parents' room at about 1:00 A.M., then going to see why there were lights on downstairs. He saw Kent's mom, Mrs. Hannah, making coffee. She explained that his father had been in a car accident, and he was in the emergency room at Grant. He kept asking if his dad was going to die, and Mrs. Hannah said she didn't know.

His dad passed away five days later from heart complications.

For several weeks, his mother tried to find work. She had jobs at a car wash, a local fast food restaurant, and a drugstore. Finally, she went back to school for a couple of years to get a master's degree in parenting education.

The next year, she received a phone call from a Hollywood producer named Richard LaSalle. He offered her a job on a cable television show called "Parenting Today."

Abruptly, Miguel stopped thinking and finished off his speech.

"And lastly, I'd like to thank my mother for her constant support. Thank you."

After a few minutes of applause and compliments and pats on the back, he modestly picked up his books and went to his fifth-period class.

Chapter 4

Miguel was disgusted that the trash he took out two days ago was still there on the curb near his parents' enormous estate at 662 Terrance Way. He decided for himself that the waste disposal union must be on strike.

Miguel cleared his throat as he opened the back door to his house, putting the key in his pocket.

"Mom! You home?"

He didn't really expect his mom to be home. Ever since his mom became host of the television show, she was never home except for Sunday nights.

Miguel went to the formal kitchen to get a snack. He bit an apple as he looked about the room. A note was on the refrigerator that read, "I'll be home early. Love, Dad." Of course it was from Richard, his new stepfather.

He sat down disenchanted to watch TV. There was a commercial for some toothpaste, a contest sponsored by a cereal company, and an ad for some new perfume. He switched over to the

Health Network. He saw something that made him groan, then he switched channels again.

Soon he heard the sound of the garage door opening, and he knew Richard was home. He went to meet him outside.

"Hey, guy, how's everything?" Richard said, trying to sound sincere.

"OK," Miguel muttered. It wasn't as though he didn't like Richard, but he couldn't believe that his mother could actually replace his dad. He had thought, after his dad died, she would just be a widow forever.

"Hey, Richard, can we talk?"

"Sure, Mike."

They sat down on the sofa in the living room.

"What's up?"

"I read my speech."

"How'd it go?"

"Great."

"Awright! Way to go, amigo!"

Richard loved to call him "amigo."

"Uh, Richard . . . I was thinking today . . . I know you never knew my friend David, from Cleveland . . ."

"No, I don't believe I ever met a 'David.' "

"Well, do you think we could have him come here sometime? For a visit? Like, to sleep over?"

"What? Mike, use your head. It's too far. Kids your age can't travel alone, not in this town anyway. Too dangerous!"

Miguel rested his chin on the arm of the couch.

"I haven't seen Grandma or Grandpa for ages, either!"

"Well, I'm sure you can discuss those things with your mom."

"Come on, I just want to be normal. I don't like living where everyone's rich. I don't want to live in the same place as movie stars and former presidents. I just want to live in an average neighborhood in an average town, and I want friends my age."

"But, Mike, you're lucky. Everybody loves L.A. It's where the action is, ya know."

"Geez . . ." Miguel opened his mouth to speak again, but then closed it and went upstairs.

Chapter 5

Dear Dave,

How are you? L.A. is great. I just saw a show called "The Fantasticks" with Mom. She was just crazy about it. How's your mom and dad? Have you been sailing on the lake lately? Have you seen Ted around anywhere? How's Agnun? Here at the Academy we don't get into middle school until 7th grade. I remember at that boys' school back in Columbus, you got to be in middle school when you were in 5th grade. That would be great!

Sorry I haven't written, but everything is so

strange here. Different from the 'burbs. Geez, I hope I see you again someday.

> Your bud,
> Mike S.

Chapter 6

On Monday morning, Miguel left home for bus #890 as usual. He had this idea in his mind about a new story he wanted to write. There would be this young girl who was stranded on an island with only two gallons of water, a mirror, and a length of wire. All he had to think of was the plot. This was how Miguel always got stuck.

He walked only a block or two when he saw some kind of riot going on down the block.

"Sam, Sam, skinny man! Sam, Sam, skinny man!" a bunch of kids shouted, as they pushed someone to the ground.

Soon a chant began to rise in volume. "Skinny man! Skinny man!"

A circle formed around a tall, stringy boy about fourteen years old. His wiry frame began to get pushed around the circle. "Skinny man! Skinny man!"

Miguel had seen this type of thing before, in Worthington. He used to be picked on all the time himself when he was little. Sometimes he would be called "Big Ears," or sometimes "Commie," for his apparent Ukrainian roots. He'd even been called "Toreador," for his Spanish-American heritage. He got over it eventually, but it really hurt him.

"Skinny man! Skinny man! Ha, ha, ha, ha!"

After a few minutes, the circle broke up and kids began to walk away, happy and smug, as the bus with the bright yellow and black paint pulled up the the stop.

Miguel ran over to hop on the bus and take his usual seat under the letter "L."

He felt very sorry for Sam, who really didn't deserve to be teased like that. It really got him thinking.

In fact, it bugged him all day.

Chapter 7

"Hi, I'm Samuel Carpenter," an unseen voice muttered.

Miguel slowly turned around to see the boy who had been teased that morning speaking to him from behind the topiary on the Academy's front lawn. He stepped toward Sam as the second dismissal bell rang out through the dreary afternoon. It was raining cats and dogs. Many boys were carrying umbrellas, but they didn't really use them. Only nerds used umbrellas at the Academy.

Sam hid his face behind the umbrella he had opened. He looked very different from the other kids. He had a large nose and big gray eyes that had a natural squint.

"Hey, Sam, c'mon out. It's OK."

Sam sheepishly came over to the Corinthian column that Miguel was standing by, as the rumble of thunder became audible.

"I guess you saw me this morning," he said.

Miguel stood silent for a minute, looking at the ground.

"Uh-huh."

"Those guys . . . they're so mean."

Sam took a pair of large glasses out of his pocket and fumbled to rest them on his nose.

Miguel felt uncomfortable.

"You're Mike, right? Student of the Year?"

"Yup."

Sam took a pen from his shirt pocket and nervously chewed on the end. Miguel could see deep bite marks all over it.

"I guess you must know I'm new around here."

You, too? Miguel was about to blurt it out, but he decided against it.

After a few moments, Sam mumbled something.

"What?" asked Miguel.

"Forget it."

"No, what did you say?"

29

"You wouldn't understand."

Miguel looked at him, ready to take his word for it.

Sam changed his mind and said, "I hate L.A."

Miguel listened with interest.

"See, I'm from Iowa. I was born on a farm in Tuskala Hills. I just hate this life."

Miguel contemplated whether Sam could really be feeling the same things he did. He had felt so alone wanting to go back to Ohio, and now someone was reaching out and giving him the opportunity to find out more about himself and why he was so dissatisfied with his new home and new life.

"Me, too. I'm from Ohio."

Sam looked pleased. He seemed to be a little less nervous. The rain was slowing, and he put his umbrella away.

"But . . . I thought you were from Mexico . . . the Yucatan part . . . or that's what I've heard."

Gossip brigade, Miguel thought.

"No," he said, "University Heights, Ohio. You know, near Cleveland."

A bolt of lightning ripped the sky apart as Miguel wiped a raindrop from his cheek.

"But, yes. I am part Spanish. But I'm also part Jewish, too."

Sam looked down at the damp ground, thinking of what to say, as a series of rumbles echoed through the dusk.

"My grandfather was part Maltese, but he wasn't my blood relative."

Now the storm was getting stronger.

Miguel looked around. The other kids had gone.

"Have you ever been to Ohio?"

"No."

"Well, I've never been to Iowa."

"Hey, Mike . . . do you like the Hawkeyes?"

"The U of I Hawkeyes? They're wimps!"

Sam looked at Miguel critically.

"You know, I used to love riding the Rapid to the Terminal Tower . . ."

"What's the Rapid?"

"The Rapid Transit. Trains that are partly cable cars, partly subways, partly . . ."

"This was in Cleveland?" Sam said.

"Uh-huh."

Another three lightning bolts lit up the late summer afternoon.

Sam looked up at the sky as he scratched his nose.

"You may think this is dumb . . . but I was just thinking. You, remembering about the Rapid and me, about the cornfields, and, well, L.A. isn't so bad . . . if we still have memories of the places we'd like to be."

"Places we'd like to be . . ."

Miguel drifted off into another daydream.

The ground seemed to shake as a clap of thunder roared across California.

Chapter 8

Dear Mike,

I'm glad you wrote. Sorry I didn't reply earlier, but things have been really hectic around here. Looks like we're moving too. Dad doesn't know where to just yet, but it could be Boston, Ft. Worth, or Houston. Now I think I know how you must have felt when you moved. I have lived in this house all my life. I have never known another home. I was sad enough when you moved, but this is too much.

Your friend,
David S. Greenspan

P.S. I'm glad you like L.A.

THIRD PLACE

THE MUSICAL FROG
by Kathy Goebel

To Mrs. Gunderson,
my favorite teacher and friend

Chapter 1

FROGS FOR SALE

Once there was a girl named Sally, and she wanted to take piano lessons. Her mom thought it was a wonderful idea. The next day, after school, Sally went to get a piano book. As she walked out of the shop, Sally counted her change. There was five dollars. On her way home Sally passed a pet store. In the window was a sign.

```
FROGS FOR SALE
$5 a frog
Frog Race on Sat. the 18
COME IN FOR DETAILS
```

Sally loved animals so she bought a frog. She named him W.A. Mozart and entered him in the contest.

As she walked home, she thought of how to train him for the race. What would be the key? "Key!" Sally exclaimed. "I'll teach and train him by music." Sally gave a hop, skip, and a jump, and scurried the rest of the way home.

When Sally got home she showed her mom the music, and the frog.

"Do you think it is a good idea to train him by music?" she asked.

Her mom answered, "Yes. And it will also keep you busy."

Sally's dad called from the kitchen, "I'll make a home for it."

Sally exclaimed, "I can put my toy piano in his house so he'll feel as if he's in the living room."

Sally's parents agreed to help in every way possible.

As the days went on, Sally played piano better and better. Mo leaped higher and higher. Sally and her frog were very good friends.

Chapter 2

THE MUSIC BOX MYSTERY

Sally woke up suddenly. She had heard tinkly music. When Sally told her parents about it, they were afraid of burglars. Sally was worried, too—about ghosts. Sally asked her parents if Mo could stay in her room, and they gladly answered, "Yes." That night Sally heard the music again, but it was louder. Sally dreamed that she saw a ghost playing on an untuned organ.

Many nights she heard the music and had the dream, and Sally wanted to put a stop to it. She was so troubled that often she couldn't play piano properly.

Sally thought a lot about her problem. Without her playing, Mo grew very lazy. Sally forced herself to practice long and hard.

One afternoon, when she arrived home from school, she heard muffled music flowing down the stairs. It gave her the creeps. Sally thought to herself as she edged noiselessly into the house, I'll get Mo and we'll find out what is making the music. Then Sally dashed up the stairs to her room and went straight to Mo's box.

The music suddenly stopped. Then slowly it started again. Sally lifted the lid to Mo's box and began to laugh. In the box she found the frog, smiling and jumping on the toy piano.

Chapter 3

THIS IS IT

The race was a week away. As Sally sat practicing piano, her mom called from the bottom of the stairs, "I think you're ready for a music teacher. I'll take you to Mrs. Peacock's tomorrow."

Sally was so excited that she almost jumped on Mo (who was jumping around too). Sally practiced the rest of the evening.

The next morning, at school, Sally couldn't answer the questions properly. After school, her mom gave her some new music. Sally took Mo along to the piano lesson, which turned out to be a disaster.

Mrs. Peacock let Sally in. Then she excused herself and went to get a glass of water. While she was gone, Sally slipped the frog into the piano. She told herself, "I'll take him out when she gets back." But when the teacher returned, she began the lesson right away. As the first few chords were played, Mo jumped out and landed on Mrs. Peacock!

"Aghh! Get him off of me!" She dropped Mo, and Sally quickly retrieved him.

Mrs. Peacock was really mad. "Leave right now!" she ordered.

Sally cried, setting Mo down, "Give me one more chance. I wanted to show you . . ."

Mrs. Peacock didn't let her finish. "I never want to see you or that frog again."

Sally gingerly picked up Mo and went outside to the car, where her mom was waiting. Sally didn't want to do anything for the rest of her life.

Chapter 4

ON YOUR MARK, GET SET, RACE!

Sally woke up on the 18th, feeling terrific. It was the day of the race! She and Mo were both ready.

Sally practiced every possible chord that would be needed in the race. Her dad cleaned Mo's cage. Her mom didn't like it, but went out and caught ten flies that she brought in and fed to Mo.

They had rented a truck to carry the piano. As Sally and her parents entered the race grounds, even Mo seemed to know what was going on. They got Mo a number and waited for the race to start. Sally felt very confident.

As the race started, Sally played the piano very fast. But she slowed down when she saw how far ahead Mo was. Five minutes passed. Mo was still leading. Then it happened: Mo came in first! Sally ran across the race track to claim *her* frog, the winner!

"Oh, Mo, I knew you could do it!"

She got her prize money and they put Mo and the piano in the truck. Then Sally asked her parents if they could stop at the toy store. When they got there, Sally bought a glass toy piano with gold and silver keys. It also had a glass case. On the key last played before Mo won, she had the store engrave the words "Mo, the Musical Frog."

When Sally got home, she picked up Mo and said, "You won! You'll always be a winner!" Then Mo fell limply against her hand. He had died.

Sally was very sad. On his grave went the glass piano.

Many years after that, Sally played a concert. She whispered to herself, "Here's to you, Mo!" Sally played the piece perfectly. She sat backstage a while with her memories. Then a reporter came up and asked, "What do you owe your musical life to?"

Sally answered proudly, "Ever since I was ten, I have loved music. I'm sixty now, but I will never forget the one who inspired me—Mo, the Musical Frog!"

The End

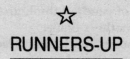

RUNNERS-UP

WHY I WHINE WHEN I DO
by Bridget Michelle Faugot

To Mrs. Karen Foret and my parents

When I was a baby, I whined for a bottle, my diaper to be changed, attention, a nooney, or to be held. You've probably noticed when babies from newborn to about twelve months start to cry and you give them one of these things, they will hush up.

When I got into nursery school, I changed the reasons why I whined. My main reason was to be first in line. (You have to think back to all these ages you were to realize these whining reasons.) If I was first in line I felt better than the rest of the whining kids.

Then when I got up into first and second grades, I whined for candy at the grocery store. The next time you go into a grocery store and you're checking out, look on the side of you and you will probably see a rack of candy. I think grocery stores do that to drive mothers crazy.

In third, fourth, and fifth grades, I simply whined till my teeth and eyes fell out for two people to sleep over. I think the reason I didn't have people sleep over often is that we always made a mess, and then when my mom told me to clean it up I started whining again.

Now I'm finally at that middle year—sixth grade —and I'm still whining. I whine to my mother because she won't let me wear bright nail polish and big earrings. I always want more and more designer clothes. I've been wanting a girl-boy party, but my mom says I'm way too young.

Wow! I just realized how much whining I'm going to do in the future. I'll have to whine for makeup, dates, and late curfews. Boy! I sure do have my work cut out for me!

THE VAN FIRE
by Justin Scott Ball

*To my parents and grandmother
and Susan Hodgin*

We've had the Van since before I was born. It is an 1978 Econoline 150 Ford Van. Mom, Dad and I loved Buud, as we called him. Buud had orange paint outside and was carpeted with a tan carpet inside. The seats swiveled and reclined and were orange with black seat belts. The seats got hot in the summer because the Van didn't have air conditioning. You could open the sunroof and the windows. The sunroof wasn't such an advantage on rainy days because it leaked.

I liked the reclining seats and the radio and cassette deck. I didn't like bumping my head on the ceiling lights, but they were handy for other things. I liked the smooth running and I liked the size.

There was a console and submarine-style back windows. The back of the Van had some special compartments which I stored some things in. There used to be a painting of the desert on the back door of the Van until some jerk in a big pickup truck hit the back of the Van while Mom was driving.

Mom wrecked the Van a lot. Dad said he liked the Van because it was big and sturdy and saved Mom's life when she was hit head on by a drunk driver. It seemed like every two years Mom was in a big wreck or something.

The last time, we were driving back from dropping Nana off at the mall and we were stopped at a stoplight when Mom noticed smoke coming up from the hood. She told me to stay in the car and she went to the guy behind us and told him that she thought the car might be on fire. Then the hood really started smoking. She told me to run. I ran to Bonanza. As I remember it, there were a lot of thistles along the grass that was between the corner we were on and Bonanza.

So we ran to Bonanza and we got to the phone booth that was just inside the door and Mom called the fire department. OUCH! I was in thongs when I was running through the thistles and weeds. Mom was wearing sandals and I was wearing thongs, seeing weeds, seeing the Van smoking, seeing Bonanza, and feeling pain.

As Mom was calling, I looked out the window of Bonanza and saw there were flames shooting out from the bottom of the Van.

About two minutes after we called, we heard sirens, and two fire trucks came up. Then the chief's car came up. Then the firemen started doing their job putting out the fire. I met the fire chief when he came up to me and gave me the pin from a fire extinguisher. He told me it was a souvenir and to keep it.

After the fire trucks left, we looked at the Van and then we called Dad. Dad said, "I liked that Van." Mom told me Dad kept saying, "I liked that Van!"

We looked back at the smoking wreckage of the Van and wondered how we were going to get home. Me and Mom thought about that question while we had a drink at Bonanza. We called Lisa Russell and she came in her truck to pick us up.

While the Van was burning, I felt helpless and sad because I couldn't do anything about it. I sort of felt afraid for my physical safety but I didn't think the Van would blow up. Once I was out of it, I was worried that I'd lose some of my valuable things still in the Van and I was happy that they made it. I did lose my Weird Al tape, which was in the cassette player and was completely destroyed along with another tape when the dashboard melted.

As I looked at the smoking wreckage, I began to miss our Van. I started thinking of all my memories of the Van.

Mom used the Van to go to yard sales. She went to yard sales every Friday evening and Saturday morning. She would hop into the Van and spend about three hours going to every single house in Moscow that had a yard sale advertised, buying every piece of junk that seemed remotely appealing. When she came back she always brought us our favorite kinds of doughnuts. Occasionally, she brought back something for us like some toys or a bulletin board or a fishing pole.

When she finally got done with yard sales, she took me to karate or any other lessons I might have that day.

The Van was my personal storeroom. Whenever I couldn't find something, I always asked Mom for the keys and went out and looked through the Van. I kept lots of things in there. I kept my cards of the different presidents in the Van. My bike helmet and my baseball equipment came and went from the Van but were there most of the time. My Weird Al tape stayed in the Van for most of its life. I had a "Rip Van Winkle" tape that I always kept in there.

In the back seat, where I always sat when we traveled, I kept my sticker collection. I had a bunch of stickers all stuck to one certain area of the sliding door. Whenever I was on a long trip and was bored with reading and had nothing to do, I'd look at my stickers. I had some stickers of cars and a "Keep out! This room is private!" sticker. I had two stickers from bananas, a Dole and a Chiquita. My dad was annoyed at the fact that whenever I opened the back door of the Van, my toys fell out on the road.

I used to play "Taco John's Restaurant" in the Van. That was done in the rearmost section. I would take out the jack and spare tire and whatever other junk that was lying in the Van that could serve any remote use in making a pretend diner. If there was anyone in the Van, I would ask what I could get for them. Then I'd pretend to make them food. Once I made the food, I'd serve it to them.

When I played "office," I climbed into the spare tire and used a toy computer I had and pretended I was in an office. The spare tire was my desk.

On long trips, I would play like I was flying a jet and the Van was the jet. I'd say, "This is your captain speaking." Mom was the copilot; I was the captain; and Dad was the navigator.

My favorite trips in the Van were the hiking trips to the Cascades. My first hike was with Dad and John Lawrence to Grasshopper Pass, Hart's Pass, and Windy Pass. On this trip, I got some fossilized snails from the top of Slate Peak.

My favorite backpacking trip in the Van was to Mount Rainier. I remember hiking over a trail with a little gulch full of snow where my dad taught me self-arrest with his ice ax. We fed the chipmunks at Second Burroughs. There was a rock bench where I sat with Dad and watched the mountain. It was huge!

I learned how to play my harmonica on a camping trip to Hat Point. I had to learn two songs for a Cub Scout requirement. I started to learn "Jingle Bells" when we left Moscow. We were driving along the Imnaha River Road when I learned "Oh

Susanna." I learned "Camptown Races" by our campfire at Black Horse Campground.

Most Tuesday afternoons in the summer, we would go in the Van on a fly-fishing trip. We would usually go with some of my dad's friends from work, including Phil Scuderi and Keith Dunker. I'd serve as the Van cook, making sandwiches and drinks for all the people on the fishing trip and waiting on them by passing out cookies and making lemonade. It was fun. I've never caught a fish on any of these trips. I have got a few bites and I have lost a few things. I'm still learning to fly-fish and looking forward to catching a fish on a fly that I've tied.

I have caught fish with my spinning outfit. A lot of the time on weekends in the summer, Mom would take my best friend, Christopher, and me to Spring Valley Reservoir in the Van. Mom would always sit on the dock in a lawn chair reading a new mystery story while we were catching something, being invaded by ducks, or falling in the water.

One time we got a visit from two Canada geese and they were even nipping at our fingers. We were feeding them Doritos. A park ranger had told us that the geese would eat anything crunchy and made out of some kind of grain. I'd caught a great rainbow trout on a mixture of some hard corn I found that was lying on the dock and some salmon eggs. One of the geese decided he wanted more than Doritos. There was a great flapping of wings, a great splashing of water, and a big *awwwk* sound. That goose walked up on the dock and ate the rest of the corn. There went my bait. No more big fish! I thought to myself.

The Van had a very entertaining leaky sunroof. Whenever it had been raining, a little puddle formed on Mom's head. Rain never seemed to come down on my head. It was entertaining watching her face. It was kind of fun watching it change from a casual smile to a deep frown as a little waterfall flowed off her head.

I used to listen to my "Rip Van Winkle" and *Gulliver's Travels* tapes in the Van's cassette player and my Weird Al tape. The tape player worked nicely. Its only disadvantage was that it didn't have a rewind. Therefore, whenever you wanted to rewind a tape, you had to turn it over and do fast forward on that side. There was a stereo booster that allowed you to adjust the speakers in the Van. I used to like to concentrate all of the music into the speakers where I was sitting.

Whenever we went on a trip, the lucky Dad got the reclining seat in the front and I got the reclining seat in back. Mom was the only one without a reclining seat because she was the driver. It was fun to lie down in the reclining seat and get forty winks while cruising down the highway at 55 miles an hour.

After I was born, I came home from the hospital in the Van, and I celebrated all of my birthdays in the Van. I remember my fourth birthday. It was just three days after we moved into the old house in Moscow, Idaho. I got a little robot from Uncle Bob, and Aunt Mica came to visit from Denver.

I also had a surprise birthday once at the Micro Moviehouse. As I was going down the aisle with my best friend, Christopher, I noticed a black tuft of hair in my favorite seat. A pair of brown eyes were looking back at me and then suddenly the head vanished behind the back of the seat. Suddenly I heard this extremely loud, "Surprise!" I looked around me and saw a lot of my friends from the classroom. The black tuft of hair and brown eyes belonged to Frances Reyes, one of my schoolmates.

We all watched "Peter Pan" and when it was over, all ten of us piled into the Van and rode home to Rotary Park where we played "Peter Pan" on the log structure.

The kids loved to ride in our Van. They thought the little round back windows made it look like a submarine.

I remember going up to Spokane to Toys R Us in the Van on my eighth birthday. I got a sound-mixing system and the "Rolling Thunder," which is a GI Joe. After we left Toys R Us, we drove for about another hour and arrived at Coeur D'Alene Lake. We always parked in the same place at the lake and I always used the back of the Van as a dressing room to put on my swimming suit. The submarine-style back windows and the regular back windows were covered with a dark film, which permitted me to see out but prevented other people from seeing in.

Mom, Dad, and Nana always walked calmly to the lake. Dad usually carried my surfboard, and I ran in top gear along the grass that was bordered from the beach by a concrete wall. The beach was about three feet below the wall. I liked to jump off the grass where the top of the wall began. Once in the water, I played "shark," which is played by scooting all the fingers of your hand together and making a "knife." I'd swim under the water with just my hand sticking up. If I was lucky, my hand looked like the fin of a shark.

The Van had a console that we could use to carry cups of liquid, like soda pop and milk and an occasional coffee. Mom got pretty steamed whenever I spilled food. Once when we were coming home from McDonald's, I was eating my hamburger and I got some mustard on the seat. I tried to hide it by sitting on it. I was drinking my pop and I spilled that on my crotch and so I stood up slightly to look at what had happened and Mom noticed the mustard. First she was mad about the mustard and then she noticed the pop on the seat and became even madder. She swore she'd never buy me another Happy Meal again. She's done that about five times now.

The Van burned on Wednesday, July 18, 1990, and that's when I elected Wednesdays my official bad day. We bought a Honda on August 2, 1990.

We drove our 1961 Chevrolet pickup from when the Van burned until we bought the Honda. Mom said, "I missed the Van!" She didn't like driving the truck because it didn't have power steering. Riding in the pickup truck was a problem because there was no air-conditioner. It was really hot and the truck always stalled. I had to listen to Mom griping that it didn't have power steering and it got too hot.

Blowing off a lot of money on the Honda was a problem. It's a nice car but it keeps having transmission problems. Dad can't take his coat off easily in the Honda like he could in the Van because the Honda is so much smaller.

My Dad and his friend Pete Kilwein are beginning a restoration project for the Van. Pete owns the body shop where the Van has been repaired after each of Mom's wrecks. They're taking another Van that has a good front end and a terrible back end and putting them together to make a totally new Van. It's been a problem having Dad blow off a lot of his time trying to fix the Van. That is wasted time because we could be doing something better if that Van hadn't burned.

A happy ending would be that the Van gets fixed and is in working order pretty soon. The day our Van burned, I was thinking I'd never ride in Buud again. Now I'm hoping I will.

THE EASY WORLD

by Taylor Allison Nolen

To Mrs. Pat Nicholson, my fantastic teacher
who helped make this story possible

I know a place where all the people are happy and no one has arguments. There are no hunters to kill the animals, and deer and buffaloes come up to you and allow you to touch them. There are absolutely no pets.

You can drive at any age above six and the car dealers always measure you to see what section of cars to look at. And each kid in school has a book and the kid does work out of it at their own pace. When school is over each kid goes to Elitch's for free. When they get bored with the rides, the kids finally go home and play until suppertime.

At breakfast a robot comes and asks, "What do you want to eat?" and the robot makes your breakfast. And, if you want, at lunch and dinner the robot does the same thing.

The people there you can depend on. They all have good manners too. They will make friends with you right away.

The grown-ups get good jobs and like their work very much. The people of this place never beep their horns; they just roll down the window and say, "Please move," very kindly.

And there are no poor people or beggars. Each family has an indoor swimming pool. And many people do work for the Salvation Army. And each person recycles everything recyclable. This world will never blow up like Earth.

Each person has a garden. A flower garden or food garden. They all are professionals at sports. They start sports at two years old.

The people get good food to eat. At the dinner table there is no fuss about eating vegetables because everyone likes the vegetables that their moms put on their plate.

And that's my favorite place.

The End

LETTERS TO HOME: VIET NAM
by Carl Grayson Bell, Jr.

Dear Mom & Dad,

They say I can come home in about 1 mo. I can't wait to see all of you again. Has anything changed since I have been gone? Say hi to all my friends & my dog Boomer.

Love,
your son John

✱   ✱   ✱

Dear John,

We are looking forward to having you home again. Everyone wants to have a party for you and I am going out to buy all your favorite foods. See you soon.

Love,
Mom & Dad

Dear Mom & Dad,

I have a friend here. His name is Jack. He wants to come with me and stay a while. Will this be ok? He is really a neat guy and he can stay in my room with me.

Love,
John

✿   ✿   ✿

Dear John,

Sure you can bring home your friend. We would love to meet him. What special would he like?

Love,
Mom & Dad

✿   ✿   ✿

Dear Mom & Dad,

Jack does have a problem. Our last day in the field he had a hand grenade go off next to him. He is now deaf but he gets along fine. Is this still ok?

Love,
John

Dear John,

War has its toll on everyone but this does not make him less of a man. We would be glad to have him.

Love,
Mom & Dad

✻ ✻ ✻

Dear Mom & Dad,

Jack also had to have his right arm amputated, so he has had to learn to write all over again. He is doing better with it.

Love,
John

✻ ✻ ✻

Dear John,

Are you sure he won't be an imposition on you? We can work around any handicap like this.

Love,
Mom & Dad

Dear Mom & Dad,

Jack also had to have his right leg amputated. He is in physical therapy to help him.

Love,
John

❀　❀　❀

Dear John,

This will make things more difficult but we will manage somehow, I am sure.

Love,
Mom & Dad

❀　❀　❀

Dear Mom & Dad,

Jack is paralyzed from the waist down. He has to be in a wheelchair to get around.

Love,
John

❀　❀　❀

Dear John,

Your father and I have discussed Jack and we feel he would be too much for us to handle. Please tell him how sorry we are and we wish him well.

Love,
Mom & Dad

```
                    Department of the Army
                    Washington, D.C.


Mr. and Mrs. John Jones, Sr.
Harrisburg, Pennsylvania

Dear Mr. and Mrs. Jones:

  We are sorry to inform you that your
son John killed himself last night.
This letter was addressed to you.
Please accept our regrets for your
loss.

                    Sincerely,
                    Sgt. Charles McMan
```

❋   ❋   ❋

Dear Mom & Dad,

I am sorry I lied to you about Jack. I am Jack. I had to find out how you would feel about my handicap so I made up Jack, but I understand. Remember I will always love you and I could not put you through the trouble of taking care of me.

Love always,
John

WHAT? SANTA'S GRAVE?

by Kristina Cavallo

*To my Grandma Kay and Grandpa John,
whom I love very much*

It was a dark rainy day on December 23. I was on my way to the graveyard where my grandpa was buried. It was the seventh anniversary of his burial.

When I arrived with my mom, there was another grave next to my grandfather's grave. There had never been one there before, so I went over to see whose grave it was. "Oh, my God," I yelled out.

"What's wrong?" my mom asked, dropping all the flowers.

"Saint Nicholas's grave!"

"What? I can't hear you," she said, quickly walking over.

My throat was dry, "Sa—Sa—Sa—Santa's grave," I finally got out.

"It's not Santa's grave. You're probably just reading the name wrong."

"I didn't! I can read, can't I?" I snapped.

"Get in the car!" my mother answered.

"But—"

"Get in the car!"

She went back to the car, mumbling, "All the flowers are ruined."

I hate her, I thought to myself. She's a big pain. I hate her, I hate her, I hate her.

She got in the car and slammed the door. "You made me ruin all the flowers!" she yelled.

"You didn't have to drop them either!" I yelled back.

"When we get home you better go straight up to your room. And no Nintendo either," she snapped, and stepped on the gas pedal.

The next day, I went over to my friend's house. We listened to the radio and had some lunch.

Around one o'clock, Jennifer's mom told us to get in the car. "We have to take a ride to the five-and-ten, and then we have to stop at the cemetery."

"Which one?" I asked.

"The Gates to Heaven," she replied.

It was where my grandpa was buried. I thought to myself, Maybe Jenny's mom will let us take a walk over to the grave next to my grandfather's grave.

When we arrived at the graveyard, we pulled up to Jenny's aunt's grave. It was only about four rows behind my grandpa's grave, so I asked if we could walk over to the grave. She said, "Okay, but I want you to be back in ten minutes."

When we got to the grave, I closed my eyes. I

was afraid that the stone really would say Saint Nicholas.

I opened my eyes wide. It said Shawn Nicolas.

I couldn't believe it. Shawn Nicolas died on December 10, 1990. My mom was right again. She's always right, I thought.

When we got back to Jennifer's house, I called my mom and told her. She said, "See? You got in trouble for nothing, just because you wouldn't listen to your dear old mother."

BIRD BUFFET
by Clair Null

To my mom and grandmothers

My new red Nikes made a soft *squish* every time I took a step on the freshly polished linoleum floors. I only had a few more rooms to go and I would be at Gee Gee's apartment. The rooms are not really apartments, but I always think of Gee Gee's as one.

I passed room 104, Dave Brinkley; I have visited him before; he has really bad hearing—then 105, Kate Rinik; she has even worse hearing, and can't see anything; I guess she must be around a hundred years old—and so on, until I had reached 107, Gee Gee's. I didn't even bother to knock; instead just went on in.

At first Gee Gee didn't even notice me, she was so wrapped up in the mystery she was reading. I walked over and planted a kiss on her rippled old cheek.

"Look, Gee Gee, I brought the stuff for the gingerbread house," I said, slowly unpacking the contents of the grocery bag I had been carrying. "Mom wouldn't bake the gingerbread so instead we can use graham crackers. I have all sorts of candy to decorate with, and I made this icing this afternoon. That was why I was a little late. We're gonna have the best gingerbread house this place ever saw! I asked Nurse Baker, and she said we could work on it in here, and that you could skip exercise as long as we were working on this. Isn't that great?"

Gee Gee nodded, smiling at me.

"Boy," I said, changing the subject entirely, "our milk carton bird feeders are sure a big hit! There must be around twenty birds out there."

"You're right!" Gee Gee said. "That was a good idea, making the feeders. Yesterday I saw three or four cardinals, eight or nine finches, and even a ladder-back woodpecker." It had been a long time since I had seen her so excited.

Before long, we were up to our elbows in icing and candy. We talked while we worked. I told her about the school Christmas parties that day, and she invited me to Christmas dinner with her the next day. They were having it early because most of the residents go to their relatives' houses over Christmas.

Our gingerbread house began to take shape. It wasn't very big, but it was beautiful. It was about six inches high, including the roof, which we had decorated with Ritz Bits as shingles. We had put two trees and a bush in the yard, and had even added a pretzel man. Although we had a lot done, there was still a lot to do, and it was time for me to leave.

"Gosh, Gee Gee, look at the time! It's almost six. I told dad that I'd be home about six-thirty. I really have to go. I'll see you tomorrow at Christmas dinner."

"Good-bye, Amy, and good luck getting home. It's snowing, so be careful," Gee Gee said to me. I hadn't realized that it was snowing and as soon as she said it was, I rushed to the window to look out. Sure enough, a fine white powder was falling.

I gathered my bookbag from where I had dropped it. I blew a kiss to Gee Gee, and left.

Outside it was a lot cooler, not cold, but cool. In a way it felt good to me. The heat at Gee Gee's is always cranked up to around 90 degrees. Elderly people must be practically cold-blooded. At first when I started coming to Plainview, I always got hot, but now I'm used to it.

I've been a volunteer at Plainview Nursing Center for two years now. I visit all of the residents, but Gee Gee is definitely my favorite. I know that it's not nice to pick favorites, but I can't help it. All the other residents are older and most of them can't hear or see, but Gee Gee has perfect sight and hearing. Some of them don't talk, and some are even nasty. I guess you can see why Gee Gee is my favorite. She probably wouldn't even have to live there if it weren't for that little heart problem. I don't know what I'd do without her.

I had reached my house by now, and so I quit dreaming and went in. As usual Dad wasn't home. He works out of town, and even though he gets off at five o'clock, he doesn't get home until around six—and seven on the days he goes shopping. I noticed that the grocery list was gone and figured that he wouldn't be home for another hour.

I took off my shoes; by now they were soaked; and laid my backpack on the table. I hardly had any homework, so I headed upstairs to read this really good book that I'm in the middle of. I didn't make it any farther than the downstairs bathroom. I went over to the mirror, and stared back at myself. I am soooo ordinary. I have an ordinary name —Amy Smith. I live in an ordinary town, and I even look ordinary. Besides all that, nothing exciting ever happens to me. The only interesting thing that ever happened to me is that, in third grade, my teacher took my class on a field trip to Plainview Nursing Center; and ever since then I have gone there and tried to cheer up the residents.

Pretty soon I got tired of staring at myself, so I wandered into my room and picked up the book that I was reading. It was really good, and quite soon I was lost in a world of fairies and unicorns.

The next morning I woke up, and just as I was getting ready to start my morning routine of getting ready for school, I realized that this was the first day of the holiday break.

"Yes! All right!" I cried with a ton of enthusiasm. The best part, though, was knowing that I hardly had any homework. Darn old Ms. Berkly had assigned a book report for when we came back, but that was all.

I took my time trying to pick out a nice outfit to wear. It was still snowing, so I decided to wear these nice pale blue overalls and a white turtleneck that my grandma had sent me as an early Christmas gift.

An hour or so later, I was dressed, fed, and on my way to Plainview. It was still snowing, so my dad drove me.

I walked on in, but instead of going to Gee Gee's room, I walked a little farther down the hall to the nurses' desk. I'm not a real nurse—kind of like a junior nurse, though. The nurses trust me to help the residents get to the dining hall, so I thought that maybe I should help them.

As it turned out, they didn't need my help after all. The residents had been so eager for their party that they had started buzzing to be taken to the dining hall at nine o'clock. It was now eleven, so I decided to go on down.

I walked over to the table that I usually sit at, but at my place there was a bow and three red and green balloons on the chair, and a sign that said Special Guest on the plate. For a minute I was hurt. Why hadn't they told me there was going to be a special guest? And why had they put them at my place? Just as I was beginning to become really upset, Gee Gee came over, smiling at me.

"Hi, hon! Go ahead and sit down. What are you

waiting for?" she said with a laugh, as if I was being silly.

"This place has been reserved for a special guest! I can't sit here!"

I didn't mean to shout, but I felt my voice rising as I spoke. I was practically yelling by the time I was finished.

"But, Amy, you are the special guest!" Gee Gee exclaimed. "Did you really think that I would let some stranger have your seat? Especially at Christmas dinner!"

"Oh, Gee Gee, this is so sweet. I've never been a special guest anywhere before. I'm so sorry."

I was very honored, and upset with myself for accusing Gee Gee. To make up for it, I gave her a big bear hug.

"O.K., enough special attention for me. I wasn't the only one to do this," Gee Gee said.

I gave her one more kiss, and began visiting with the other guests. Everyone seemed to be really excited about Christmas, whether they had guests coming or not.

Dinner was really good. There was everything you usually have at a holiday dinner, plus substitutes for people who couldn't have sugary things or anything else that they couldn't have. I really admired the cooks and how hard they worked for everyone.

The food was great, but the part of the meal that I will always remember was after dinner and everyone was just finishing off their desserts. The head nurse stood up and asked for our attention.

"May I have your attention, please. We here at the Plainview Nursing Center would like to thank someone who is very special to all of us. Amy Smith, would you please stand up so everyone can get a good look at you."

I stood up at my place, wondering what she would say next.

"Amy is a very special young girl. For two years she has come after school and on the weekends to visit with the residents. She has become a good friend to all of us. We want to thank you, Amy, so we got you a little gift."

At that moment Gee Gee stood up and handed me a long rectangular box wrapped in red and green paper. Inside was a finch feeder.

"It's perfect! I love it. I can hang it here, outside where everyone can see it. Thank you all so much."

I sat back down feeling great. It certainly had been a great day.

I stayed at Plainview till almost four o'clock, when it quit snowing. I had really enjoyed myself. It's no wonder, really—the award, dinner, visiting with everyone. And Gee Gee and I had spent almost an hour watching the birds that came to my new bird feeder. I knew, though, that I had to get home before dark, and I just felt like some exercise.

I said good-bye to all my friends and thanked

them for the gift, and in no time at all I was on my way home.

It was several days before I had time to visit Plainview again—Christmas Eve, in fact. I had a special gift for Gee Gee, and I wanted to take it to her. It was a small gold cardinal on a chain. I had wrapped it in a little box, with wrapping paper with birds on it, and I knew that she would love it.

It was mid-afternoon before I got there, and I headed straight for Gee Gee's room. There was something different about the center, but I couldn't quite put my finger on it.

Soon I discovered that Gee Gee wasn't in her room, so I checked the activity room, and the dining hall, but I couldn't find her anywhere. I decided that I should check the nurses' desk before panicking.

Ms. Repie was behind the counter, preparing medicine cups.

"Excuse me, do you know where Gee Gee is? I've looked everywhere, and I just can't find her," I said.

"Oh, hon, no one told you, did they? Dear, last night Gee Gee had a heart attack. The doctor rushed right over from the hospital, but she just didn't make it. Gee Gee died at about four this morning. Is there anything I can do? You must be so upset; you loved her so much. We all did."

It took me about thirty seconds to let it sink in. Then I turned and ran out of the building. I ran all the way home, up the stairs and into my room. Out of breath, I sat down on my bed. Tears streamed down my cheeks. One word raced through my mind. Gone. Gee Gee was gone.

"No," I whispered. "No. She can't be gone. She was fine. She wouldn't . . ." I couldn't say it. I couldn't admit to myself that she was dead. It wouldn't register in my head. Instead of thinking about her being gone, I thought up excuses of where she could be. "I bet she went home to her family for the weekend," I told myself. "Or maybe she went to the park. She loves the park. She might have gone to play bingo at the community center. She is very good at bingo."

I continued to think up excuses for her disappearance. Finally I just decided that the nurse wasn't fully informed and that she really didn't know.

It wasn't till two days later that I finally realized that she was gone. Really gone.

"Amy," Mom said. She had just gotten home. "Amy, I am so sorry about Gee Gee. Why didn't you tell me she had died?" She walked over and got ready to hug me, but I pushed her away.

"NO!" I screamed at the top of my lungs. "She didn't die! She wouldn't do that to me! Gee Gee didn't die!" I ran out of the kitchen and up to my room. I fell on the floor, crying uncontrollably. I gasped for breath. I heard footsteps on the stairs. I listened as they came slowly to my room. It was

Mom. She wrapped her arms around me, hugging me ever so lightly.

"Baby," she said after a minute of silence, "let her go. It's O.K. to cry, but don't force yourself to not believe the truth. People die. You can't stop that."

She got up slowly and left the room. I did not get up. I kept crying, silently, all the while thinking about what she had said. Mom is a doctor. Sometimes her patients die. Suddenly, my explanations made no sense. Now I was crying harder. Why did Gee Gee do this to me? Why did she have to go and die? Gee Gee was healthy and many at Plainview were not. Why couldn't they die? It just wasn't fair.

I quit crying, and walked over to my mirror. I stared back at myself, wanting to scream. I was mad at everyone. Then, I remembered something my best friend had said once, "Some things just happen. Sometimes you can't change them. You just have to go on." I realized now what she meant. I just had to go on. Still, I was angry and upset, and confused.

Dazed, I walked around my room, looking for something that wasn't there. Looking for Gee Gee. On my bookshelf I found what I needed, an old maroon photo album that had been a present from Gee Gee.

"Mom," I called downstairs. "Mom, can you come here?"

"I'll be right up," she called to me.

I just needed someone to hold me for a minute, to tell me everything would be O.K. I was clutching the photo album when Mom came in. She immediately sensed what I wanted and sat down next to me on the bed.

Carefully, I opened the book to the first page. On it was a picture of Gee Gee when she was two or three years old. Slowly, together, we flipped through the book. I saw Gee Gee when she was all dressed up for the prom, at her sister's wedding, holding her niece. There were pictures of her all through her life. Near the end of the album, I came upon a picture that made me stop and stare. It was a picture of Gee Gee and me a year ago. I began to cry. Mom tightened her grip on me. Amazingly, I made it through the rest of the book. I thanked Mom, and she gave me a kiss and went downstairs.

I felt a hand on my back, and discovered that it was Mom.

"Honey, I have to go to the hospital real early. How are you feeling this morning?"

My mouth was filled with slime from sleeping, so instead of answering her I just smiled.

"Good. You know, Amy, when a person dies you don't have to forget them. You can still be with them by remembering them and the things you did together. Gee Gee can still live in your heart." With that she got up and left.

While I brushed my teeth, I thought about what

Mom had said. I decided that I was ready to go on. I needed something to remind me of Gee Gee. A bird flew past the bathroom window, and I realized what I wanted to do.

By nine o'clock I was on my way to the hardware store. It was a nice day for walking, and I made good time. I bought two bags of thistle seed, and headed for Plainview.

The sidewalk leading up to the door was icy and I had to be careful. I made it inside safely, and went to the nurses' desk. I borrowed a paper cup and went on.

The door to Gee Gee's room was closed. I felt tears in the corners of my eyes, but would not let them fall. I told myself that I was doing this for Gee Gee and me, and that it wouldn't help to cry.

I walked around the outside of the building to the bird feeders Gee Gee and I had made. I was quiet and careful, and some of the birds stayed where they were. I filled up the new finch feeder.

As I walked back inside, I could have sworn I heard Gee Gee.

"You've got yourself a regular old bird buffet, Amy," she said to me.

An image of Gee Gee sitting in her chair reading one of her novels came to me. Thinking of her like that made me feel better.

"Thanks, Gee Gee," I said.

WORLD WAR THREE: THE END

by Nicole Peterson

Thanks, Mrs. Patton

"It's a beautiful day in the neighborhood, a beautiful day for a—" *Click*. I hate that show! Mr. Rogers is very, very stupid.

I went outside to get the paper. I glanced at the front page as I went in. Another article about the new Iraqi president, Anteum Hussein (Saddam Hussein's second nephew) and the Israeli president making peace. This paper says that they plan to join countries in the near future and call it Israq. Ya, right!

"Pepper!" I called. "Come and eat!" Pepper is my dog, and when I get home from school it is my job to feed him.

After we had both eaten our after-school snacks we went out to our nuclear war shelter so I could do my homework. I always wondered if it would work, and hoped I wouldn't have to try it out.

Just as I was finishing my math, I remembered something. Dinner! I rushed into the house and put some water on to boil. Then I heated up the spaghetti sauce. After that I put the spaghetti into the boiling water. I set the timer and went into the movie room.

I turned on "The Huxtables." My mother told me that a long time ago there was a television show called "The Cosby Show" with these actors' great-grandparents on it. I don't know if I believe her.

The show was a rerun that I had seen before. I went outside to ride my hoverboard. I was coming back towards the house when I saw Mom's car pulling into the garage. I sailed in and wiped out just inside the garage. Mom cursed and then said something about how she never should have gotten it for me.

"Mom!" I said. "This is the 2030's, not the 20th century!"

"Honey, what's for dinner?" she asked, trying to change the subject.

"Spaghetti," I replied. Then we went inside and ate. During dinner I asked if we could go to the beach or San Diego this Saturday. She said, "We'll see," which almost always means, "No!"

The next Friday I was doing my homework when Mom burst in.

"Mom!" I said, "What are you doing home so early?"

"Haven't you heard?" she asked.

"Heard what?"

"Israel and all the Arab countries have decided to invade America!"

"Will any other countries help us?" I exclaimed.

"Well, maybe. England probably will, but the U.S.S.R. won't. You know about all the trouble they have been having on their own!"

"What'll we do?"

"We will probably have to live in our nuclear shelter until this thing blows over," she said.

"Will I go to school?" I asked.

"No," she replied. "I want you home, safe, with me. Now go get as much food as you can carry, and I'll get our clothes. Hurry!"

Just then we heard an explosion. It didn't sound too far away!

"Ahh!" we cried in unison. Then we ran and did our tasks quickly.

After taking the food out, I got Pepper and the TV and radio. The TV newscaster said something about war breaking out. Duh, I thought. Then the screen went blank. We couldn't find a radio station either! We were hearing explosions all over now and, frankly, I was scared!

"Oh no!" we heard the Soviet president say. We had just gotten a radio station. "I pressed the wrong button! In a few minutes the world will blow up two times!"

So that was the end. I am in heaven now and get to see my friends often. God let the Soviet president come, because he says it was a mistake. I guess I believe him.

Guess what? Pepper is here too. He lives with all his dog friends now, but I visit him frequently.

Well, Mom is calling me to do my chores now, so I will be leaving. Bye!

SHE SAID SHE WAS COMING BACK

by Jonathan Simmons

Once I used to live in an *hogarcito.* That is a Spanish word for orphanage. It was not fun at all! It was smoky and there were lots of people. It was crowded and messy. I liked the people and I liked the food. Sometimes people tried to talk to us and we did not even know them.

This is where my story begins: A long, long time ago, I used to live in a little place where a mother had her baby. The mother was just sixteen years old when her baby came. The father was only nineteen. The mother and father had to quit school to take care of me. They named me Jonathan.

It was a sad time for me and my mom because my dad left us. He left because he thought taking care of babies was too much work. A week after he left, my mom had another baby. She named him Jeffree.

After about a month, my mom left Jeffree with some neighbors to take care of him.

My mom was frustrated because she couldn't

take care of two babies, or even one. She took me to the hogarcito where they could take care of me.

I did not know what was going on. I started to cry. I did not feel safe without my mom. My mom picked me up and kissed me and said, "I'll come back for you." She had tears in her eyes when she talked to me. I was really scared!

I made lots of friends at the hogarcito. One day while I was playing, a truck pulled into the compound. Out of the truck popped my little brother, Jeffree. I was really excited to see Jeffree. It had been a long time since I had seen him and he had grown up a lot. Jeffree became my best friend. I told him that our mom was coming back for us. He believed me.

One day we were at a fair. When we got on the bus to go back to the hogarcito, the bus went somewhere else. Jeffree and I didn't know what was happening and we felt scared.

When the bus stopped we heard our names on the loudspeakers. We went to a new home in the big city. They had new rules for us that we didn't understand. The lady who took care of us was called "Mommy Alicia." Mommy Alicia helped us get ready for new parents.

After a while some parents came and talked to us. We were very happy because we thought that they were our "real" parents. They took us outside to a little corner store and bought us gum and ice cream. I got myself dirty. It was not a pretty sight.

We went and climbed a tree and I said, "Good morning," in English. My new parents were amazed that I could speak any English. My new dad, Poppi, gave me a "thumbs-up" sign. I was confused because I didn't know what that meant then. We had lots of fun that day and then my new parents had to leave.

The next day my new parents came back and took us to a restaurant we had never been to before—McDonald's. Jeffree and I both got the biggest hamburgers but we did not know how to eat a hamburger so we pulled them apart and ate each part separately. My new parents then took us to a playground outside of the restaurant. We had never seen such a fun playground!

That was almost four years ago. My new parents adopted me and my little brother, Jeffree. It hasn't always been easy for me. I had to learn a whole new language, English. It was hard at first because I didn't understand anybody, and everything was different.

We experienced lots of new things when we came to America. One of the fun things we learned to do was to ride a bike. It was really hard for us because we had never ridden bikes before. One day our new parents took us to a park up in the mountains. It was wintertime and we saw snow for the first time.

I really love my adopted mom and dad. They have helped me a lot. We have a nice family but I still miss my birth mom and dad. I find myself still mad at my birth mom because she told me that she was coming back. She lied to me.

I wonder if my birth mom ever thinks of me. I wonder if I'll ever see her or if she even wants to see me. I also wonder if she will ever look for me and Jeffree. I still miss her every day. Someday I will travel to Costa Rica and see if I can find her. I'll tell her, "I still love you."

☆
POETRY WINNERS

CAN'T WAIT

Changing my instrument
From a family of strings
To a family of winds.
Can't wait.

In middle school
From violin to oboe.
Can't wait.

After the hot blazing summer,
After my birthday,
To play the woodwind instrument.
Can't wait.

Away from Mrs. Lyman,
Away from the violin,
Away from violinist sister,
Can't wait.

To Mr. Schneider,
To the oboe,
To freedom from my sister—
Can't wait.

Yukiko Adachi

RUNNING

The gun BANGS loudly.
    I start to run.
Then I pass three people . . .
    seven . . .
        twelve . . .
Wow . . . I'm in fourth place.
    Holy cow, I don't believe it.

People are throwing water on me
    and one man throws Coke.
        I'm glad. It feels good.

I'm on my seventeenth mile.
    Great . . .
I slip back to seventh.
    Boy, am I mad . . .

I run hard, harder.

Into second.
    Awesome . . .

Then I become the leader.
    Rad . . .
And then, I'm back to third.
    Shoot!

Here comes the finish line.
    I run as hard as I can . . .

"TIE FOR SECOND!" someone shouts.
    I don't believe it.
        I am so proud!

                Erik Leve

COURAGE

To my brother, Jon Griffith

When I am sad and down and afraid,
I turn to courage.
It takes courage to stand up and make a friend.
It takes courage to stand up for someone.
It takes courage not to fight back.

Courage is a power that's inside of you.
You are the only one who can see it.

                Joshua Griffith

THE SEA

For Grandma, who loves the sea

The sea . . . it never stays the same
for long,
It's always changing from rough
to calm.

The tide goes in.
The tide goes out.
It leaves sea shells
all about.

The sea is alive.
There are "things" inside—
So many to wonder at,
Too many to hide.

The sea never ends;
It begins and begins.
And the sea brings the gulls
And the storms and the winds.

And the children laughing,
And the old folks walking,
And the young boys fishing,
And the old waves talking.

And the little girls counting
The shells on the sand
As they walk with their moms
Side by side, hand in hand.

Rozzie Jungwirth

LAMBING

Every night
Me and my dad
Lope out to a stinky barn,
Bare and cold.
It smells like dirty dust.
We go lambing on
Spring nights.
Ewes are bearing.
Newborn lambs
Are crying about,
No wool
To keep them cozy.
Poor things.

Cody Bohn

SPRUCE FOREST

*To my parents
and Mr. Simcik, my English teacher*

The giant spruce trees surround me.
They tower high above my head like
    majestic kings and queens.
Yet there are small trees just beginning
    their long life on this planet.
Adventurous needles jump from the trees,
    dancing the whole way down.

Jared Markham

SEPTEMBER

To Mrs. Lenore Kinnison,
the person who helped make this possible

Summer is coming to an end.
Every bear is creeping into his den.
People will soon be raking leaves
That have tumbled off the trembling trees.
Autumn is coming near.
My Grandma is coming here!
Boys on my street are loud—
Everybody forms a crowd.
Rice is on the stove and frost is on the clover;
Summer, at last, is definitely over!

Andrew Wild

WHAT IS ROUND?

To my Grandma "O"

These are round:
spaghetti and meatballs on a round plate,
buttons on a plaid shirt,
red balloons on a string,
clocks ticking time,
pancakes piled high,
nine planets in a line,
the full moon,
wheels,
eyeglasses,
26 heads studying,
52 eyes looking at the sky.

Chris Bailey

OTHERWISE

*To my teacher Joyce Rakes
and both my grandmothers,
Faye Morrison and Francis Olsen*

There must be magic;
Otherwise,
How could day turn into night?

Or how could sailboats
Otherwise
Go sailing out of sight?

Or how could peanuts
Otherwise
Be covered up so tight?

Kevin C. Olsen

TO SOMEONE

With love to my grandmothers,
Frances Udler and Dorothy Sargon

To someone, being good is being bad;
To someone, being happy is being sad;
To someone, just starting is being done;
To someone, a little is a ton.
So remember what's good or bad to say,
Because everyone is different in their own
   special way.

To someone, something hard is a piece of cake;
To someone, swimming a river is swimming a
   lake;
To someone, junk is a treasure;
To someone, a hard task is pleasure.
So think about what you say before you speak.
People deserve respect too.
There are others on this earth besides you.

Miriam Sargon Udler

PEOPLE WHO
DON'T UNDERSTAND

To my family—
people who try to understand

They say I'm just a baby,
Like that's nothing at all;
But if they'd look past my cry,
They'd see how hard I really try.

They say I'm just a child,
Like that's nothing at all;
But if they'd look past my braids,
They'd find someone who gets great grades.

They say I'm just a girl,
Like that's nothing at all;
But if they'd look inside of me,
They'd find the woman I'm gonna be.

                              Tara Brune

RANNI AND ME

To Ranni Devereaux

Me in Ranni's black bikini,
she in my suit—pink with paint splats of colors.
Us wearing jean skirts and white tees,
pretending to be rock stars,
dancing to music on her queen-sized bed
in the room that she shared with her brother,
the curtain dividing their beds.
Her dollhouse with its miniatures,
makeup on our faces,
Barbies on the floor,
dress-up shows for her dad and mom.
One hand of mine holding Ranni's red hair,
the other
snapping
the balloon barrette,
then watching her red hair
spilling out
over her shirt.

When sleepovers
were at her house,
we'd talk till twelve at night—
then midnight snack time!
Me and Ranni telling secrets, and laughing.
Then her dad became a minister
and she moved away to Las Vegas, Nevada,
and became a memory to me.

I miss her.

Carrie Spritzer

THE SWEET AND SOUR WORLD: THREE POEMS

*To my mom, Harriet; dad, Mark; sister, Jennifer;
Class 6–26; all my friends; and my teacher
Mrs. Berkowitz*

1 · The Nature of This World

In this big forest savage world
    where people prey on other people,
On this earth
    where everyone is,
I cannot, just cannot
    hold my head up high
        and walk unfearing
    or I'll be caught,
like a fly wrapped in a tongue of a frog.
This is me in this big forest savage world
    where you cannot even take a berry
        off a tree and eat it—
    You just can't—
You just can't trust anybody
    in this big forest savage world
        where I live.

2 · Sweet Chocolate and Other Treats

Swish, wish, Swiss Miss Pudding, chocolate bars,
    ummmmm
That luscious, gooey,
    creamy milk chocolate that I love.
Seven-layer chocolate cake, lollypops
    Ever so delicious.
My face so full of chocolate
    I look like
        a bowl of hot chocolate swirl.
Every single morning
    I start the day with chocolate milk
        and coffee.
And at night I end it with a kiss!

3 · Quick

"Quick! Quick! Quick!"
Day and night that's all I hear:
"Do your homework. Quick!"
"Come down here. Quick!"
"Get dressed. Quick!"
And in the morning Mom says,
"Drink your Quik, quick! Quick! Quick!"

Eric Schips

SUMMER VACATION

*To our Moms and Dads,
and to our teacher Mrs. Hall*

My summer vacation was dull this year;
Leaves filled up the pool.
My summer vacation was dull this year;
I lost my favorite tool.
I could not go away this year;
I never had the time.
I could not buy good things this year;
My allowance was a dime.
I did not play too well this year;
My sister made me lose.
I could not play alone this year;
My Nintendo blew a fuse.
My dog got sick and died this year,
My cat did too.
I wish it was a better summer;
And how about you?

**Patrick Andrew Thronson and
Jonathan Ragan-Kelley**

☆
ABOUT THE AUTHORS

About the Authors

Yukiko Adachi, the author of "Can't Wait," was born in Yokohama, Japan, on August 20, 1979. She lives in Tenafly, New Jersey, where she attends Malcolm S. Mackay Elementary School. She enjoys swimming, drawing and painting, reading and writing, and playing the violin; and she hopes to be an artist or violinist.

Chris Bailey, who wrote "What Is Round?," lives in McPherson, Kansas, and goes to McPherson Middle School. He was born on October 26, 1978, in Marshall, Missouri. He likes to go fishing, biking, and swimming; and wants to be a conservation agent.

Justin Scott Ball was born on July 7, 1981, in Pullman, Washington. He lives in Moscow, Idaho, and is a student at St. Mary's School. His story, "The Van Fire," is true. Besides writing, his interests include fly tying and fishing, reading, bike riding, and playing the trombone. He hopes to go to Stanford University and become a lawyer.

Carl Grayson Bell, Jr., who wrote "Letters to Home: Viet Nam," lives in Walla Walla, Washington, where he was born on February 5, 1979. When he wrote his story, he was a student at Prospect Point Elementary School, and now he goes to Garrison Junior High School, both in Walla Walla. He likes baseball, swimming, and fishing; and would like to be a professional baseball player.

Cody Bohn, the author of "Lambing," was born on

May 11, 1980, in Billings, Montana. He now lives in Winnett, Montana, and goes to Winnett Grade School.

Tara Brune, who wrote "People Who Don't Understand," lives in Murtaugh, Idaho, and attends Hazelton Grade School in Hazelton, Idaho. She was born on August 12, 1980. She likes writing, reading, baking, being with her family, and participating in church activities and Girl Scouts. She wants to go to college and "become as good a teacher as all of mine have been."

Kristina Cavallo, the author of "What? Santa's Grave?," was born on February 1, 1979, in White Plains, New York. She lives in West Harrison, New York, and attends Louis M. Klein Middle School. She plays the flute and the piano, and hopes someday to become a writer.

Bridget Michelle Faugot, who wrote "Why I Whine When I Do," is a student at Catholic High School in New Iberia, Louisiana, where she lives. She was born in Baton Rouge, Louisiana, on September 8, 1979. She enjoys cheerleading, dancing, and writing; and wants to be a nurse anesthetist.

Kathy Goebel, the author of "The Musical Frog," lives in Brooklyn Park, Minnesota, where she attends Palmer Lake Elementary School. She was born in Minneapolis, Minnesota, on October 31, 1980. Her interests include reading, writing, talking with friends, and traveling. She would like to be a teacher ("because I've liked all of mine") and a writer.

Joshua Griffith, who wrote "Courage," was born on May 9, 1979, in St. Joseph, Missouri. He now lives in Hyrum, Utah, and goes to Spring Creek Middle School in Providence, Utah. He enjoys soccer and other sports, writing, drawing, reading, playing the piano, and doing science experiments. He hopes to become a scientist.

Rozzie Jungwirth, who wrote "The Sea," was born in Weaverville, California, on February 2, 1982. She lives in Sherwood, Oregon, and attends C.S. Lewis Community School in Newberg, Oregon. She likes arts and crafts, people, and animals (especially horses); and wants to be "a veterinarian who paints and sings."

Erik Leve, the author of "Running," lives in Swampscott, Massachusetts, and goes to Swampscott Middle School. He was born in Lynn, Massachusetts, on November 15, 1977. He likes collecting baseball cards and reading, and besides running he enjoys baseball, tennis, and golf. His immediate goal is to do well enough in school so that he can attend an Ivy League college.

Jared Markham, who wrote "Spruce Forest," was born on June 23, 1979, in Norwich, Connecticut. He lives in Colchester, Connecticut, where he is a student at William J. Johnston Middle School. He skis and plays the saxophone, and likes reading, soccer, baseball, and magic. His ambition is to become a veterinarian. His hope is for a clean and healthy environment.

Taylor Allison Nolen, the author of "The Easy World," lives in Littleton, Colorado, and attends Northridge Elementary School in Highlands Ranch, Colorado. She was born on April 6, 1982, in Denver, Colorado. She plays the piano and skis, and also likes softball, soccer, reading, writing, and crafts. She would like to be a house designer, a model, or a movie star.

Clair Null lives in Blandinsville, Illinois, and goes to Northwestern High School in Sciota, Illinois. At the time she wrote "Bird Buffet," she was a student at Northwestern Elementary School in Good Hope, Illinois. She was born in Macomb, Illinois, on June 5, 1979. She enjoys reading, writing, tap dancing, ballet, and playing the saxophone. Her goals for now are to keep dancing and to keep writing, and to do what she can to help make the world a better place to live.

Kevin C. Olsen, who wrote "Otherwise," was born in Sanford, North Carolina, on June 13, 1979. He lives in Tulsa, Oklahoma, where he attends Clinton Middle School. He likes reading, swimming, using a computer, playing Nintendo, writing, music, and girls; and he sings with the Tulsa Boys Singers. For the future he is thinking about being a doctor or lawyer or writer or an architect.

Nicole Peterson, the author of "World War Three:

The End," is a student at Elkhorn Middle School in Elkhorn, Nebraska, where she lives. She was born on January 25, 1979, in Omaha, Nebraska. She likes talking on the telephone, shopping, movies, and "Archie" comics, as well as volleyball, basketball, and tennis. She hopes to be an interior designer.

Jonathan Ragan-Kelley, the co-author of "Summer Vacation," was born in Palo Alto, California, on March 21, 1982. He lives in Salt Lake City, Utah, where he attends Rowland Hall St. Mark's School. He enjoys music, art, and reading, and basketball and baseball. He wants "to learn as much as I can and be a good friend."

Eric Schips, who wrote "The Sweet and Sour World: Three Poems," was born on August 24, 1979, in Brooklyn, New York. He still lives in Brooklyn, where he is a student at Rabbi Harry Halpern Day School of the East Midwood Jewish Center. He is a New York Mets fan and a fan of the Beatles' music, and a collector of baseball cards, coins, and comic books. He likes fishing, traveling on vacation, writing, and meeting authors. He hopes to be a lawyer and a writer.

Michael H. Shecket lives in Worthington, Ohio, and goes to Worthingway Middle School. At the time he wrote "Places We'd Like To Be," he was a student at Worthington Estates Elementary School. He was born in University Heights, Ohio, on May 18, 1979. He likes to write and to program computers; and his ambitions are "to go to a good college, study law, have my own practice, and write as a hobby."

Jonathan Simmons was born in Puntarenas, Costa Rica, on October 6, 1980. His story, "She Said She Was Coming Back," is true. When he wrote it, he was a student at Treasure Mountain Middle School in Park City, Utah, where he lives, and now he attends Hilltop School in Salt Lake City, Utah. He enjoys building model airplanes and writing stories, and he likes all sports but especially skiing, football, gymnastics, and swimming. He wants to be a father ("two children would be enough") and an airline pilot.

Carrie Spritzer, the author of "Ranni and Me," lives in Lawrenceville, New Jersey, and goes to Princeton Friends School in Princeton, New Jersey. She was born in Princeton on February 4, 1980. Her interests include gardening, cooking, baby-sitting, computers, gymnastics, and ice skating. She would like to be a teacher and start her own school.

Patrick Andrew Thronson, the co-author of "Summer Vacation," lives in Salt Lake City, Utah, where he is a student at Rowland Hall St. Mark's School. He was born in Salt Lake City on September 11, 1981. He likes basketball, card collecting, reading, chess, and math. His plans are "to continue to enjoy life and learn as much as I can."

Miriam Sargon Udler, who wrote "To Someone," was born in Boston, Massachusetts, on October 21,

1981. She lives in Newton, Massachusetts, where she attends John Ward School. She enjoys collecting rocks, coins, and stamps, and playing soccer and basketball, and writing poetry. She hopes to go to college and become a lawyer.

Andrew Wild, the author of "September," lives in Woodstock, Ohio, and goes to Ridgewood School in Springfield, Ohio. He was born in Springfield on March 24, 1981. He likes fishing, bowling, baseball, reading, chess, cards, karate, and swimming. He thinks he would like to be an attorney.

Erin Ashley Williamson, who wrote "Almost an Angel," was born on September 27, 1981, in Dallas, Texas. She lives in Highland Village, Texas, where she is a student at Christa McAuliffe Elementary School. Her present interests include horseback riding, swimming, biking, skating, gymnastics, exploring, creative writing, singing, and Girl Scouts. Her future hopes are equally wide-ranging: teacher, airplane pilot, writer, astronomer, and oceanographer.

☆

HONORABLE MENTIONS

The work of these seventy-seven young writers received honorable mention in the Young Authors of America Contest:

Celia Adelson, Cranston, RI
Jeremy Alger, Clio, MI
Elizabeth Altemus, Bloomfield, NY
David Atterbury, Kansas City, MO
Erika Beras, Bayside, NY
Amy Billimoria, Waynesboro, PA
Tim Boyle, Mamaroneck, NY
Chandra M. Brown, Wasilla, AK
Jamie Buck, Stamford, CT
Stacie Buckna, Granger, IN
Jenny Bukowski, Webster, NY
Alaina Marie Burt, Hill City, MN
Seth Ciotti, Allison Park, PA
Christina DeAnn Clark, Eldridge, MO
Kara Alison Connolly, Charlottesville, VA
Jess Cromwell, Ft. Morgan, CO
James Dallal, Williamstown, MA
Jennifer Vanessa D'Anna, Lincoln Park, NJ
Caterina M. Delia, Mt. Clemens, MI

Virginia Drouet, Three Rivers, CA
Christopher Dusek, Denver, CO
Norah Esty, Bozeman, MT
Anna Floyd, Elkton, MD
Kerri Glogowski, Stafford Springs, CT
Michael Goltermann, Pensacola, FL
Dominick Grant, Portland, CT
Katy Grodnick, Miami, FL
John Hagan, Colchester, CT
Lisa Hanson, Clinton, WA
Stephen M. Hauss, West Hills, CA
Kenny Hebb, Denver, CO
Jonathan Holland, Pittsburgh, PA
Liem Huynh, Jackson, GA
Frederick W. Jackson, Brooklin, ME
Ethan Johnson, Dunmore, WV
Brianna Kleinshmidt, Benicia, CA
Carina Lamendola, Norfolk, NY
Joel Larimore, St. Paul, MN
Michael J. Lorsbach, Omaha, NE
D'Essende Love, Monticello, AR
Jillian Mallozzi, Norwalk, CT
Jonathan McCord, Seymour, TX
Eric Merkley, Phelps, NY
Kendra Meyer, Mason, OH
Luke Moen, Skowhegan, ME
Carlos Molina, Round Rock, TX
Karyn Nugent-Ling, Clarence, NY
Zack Oliver, Portland, ME

Casey Olsen, Snowville, UT
Adrian Perkins, Springfield, VT
Jeremy Peterson, Lindstrom, MN
Lucas Peterson, Spring, TX
Kenny Plourd, Newington, CT
Danielle Putz, Salt Lake City, UT
Michael Rockwell, Conneaut, OH
Sandra Rohloff, St. Helens, OR
Erin Rozler, Avon, NY
Jennifer Russ, St. Louis, MO
Nicolas A. Salomon, Rochester Hills, MI
Michael A. Schade, Denio, NV
Stephanie Schneider, Moscow, ID
Greg Schroeder, Ottawa, OH
Kit Sielski, Montrose, MI
Julene Skrzyniecki, Pittsford, MI
Rachel Smerz, Milwaukee, WI
Bonnie Spencer, West Chester, PA
Erin Spieth, Monroeville, IN
Adrian Staff, Honolulu, HI
Adrienne Stemen, Westerville, OH
Randy Stookey, Forest City, IL
Travis Teeter, McKean, PA
James Ulmen, Boise, ID
Katie D. Wassel, Tenafly, NJ
Elizabeth Webb, Loveland, OH
Adam Wilson, Gardiner, ME
Jenni Wisniewski, Milford, OH
Rosy Wyland, Molalla, OR